The Hare
and the
Tortoise

Sticker Storybook

Jonathan Stroud
Caroline Jayne Church

Ask a grown-up to help you remove the
sticker pages from the middle of this book.
As you read, match the stickers to the story.

WALKER BOOKS
AND SUBSIDIARIES
LONDON · BOSTON · SYDNEY · AUCKLAND

Hare and Tortoise were going to have a race.
Hare was very excited.
"I'm going to win," he cried.
Tortoise said nothing.
Fox waved his big blue flag and the race
began. Hooray! As the crowd cheered,
Hare ran off faster than the wind.
Soon, Tortoise was left far behind.

Can you find the flag on the sticker page?
Put it in the picture.
Can you find two little birds watching the race?
Put them in the picture, too.

When Hare had run a little way, he saw
the baby rabbits playing hide-and-seek.
"What fun!" said Hare. "Let me join in!"
Hare spent a long time looking for
the baby rabbits.

Find three rabbits on the sticker page. Where do you think they are hiding? How many rabbits are there altogether?

Then Hare remembered the race.
He ran on again, faster than the wind.
When he had run a little way, he saw
the Bear family having a picnic.
"What fun!" said Hare. "Let me join in!"
Hare spent a long time eating
the Bears' food.

Can you find three picnic goodies to put on the rug?

Then Hare remembered the race again.
He ran on faster than the wind.
When he had run a little way, he saw
two frogs fishing in the lake.
"What fun!" said Hare. "Let me join in!"
Hare and the frogs fished for
a long time.

Between them they caught a fish,
a boot and an old car tyre.
Can you find them?
Who do you think caught the fish?

Then Hare remembered the race again.
He ran on faster than the wind.
When he had run a little way, he saw the
squirrels and badgers playing football.
"What fun!" said Hare. "Let me join in!"
Hare spent a long time playing football,
and scored three goals.

Can you find the ball?
Can you find two lost
caps? To whom do
they belong?

Then Hare remembered the race again.
He ran on faster than the wind.
But he gasped in amazement.
He could see Tortoise crossing
the finishing line.
Tortoise had walked past
Hare and won the race!

Can you find Tortoise?
There are lots of balloons
tied near the finish.
Find two more and put
them in the picture.

Hare crossed the line in second place.
"Well done, Tortoise," said Hare. "You
ran very well."
"Thank you, Hare," said Tortoise. "So did you."
"Well," said Hare, "I may not have won, but
I had a lot of fun on the way!
Let's have another race soon!"

Fox gave Tortoise a gold medal.
Can you find it?
Find Hare's silver medal. too.

For Stephen
J.S.
For William
C.J.C.

First published 1998 by Walker Books Ltd,
87 Vauxhall Walk, London SE11 5HJ
This edition published 2006

2 4 6 8 10 9 7 5 3 1

Text © 1998 Jonathan Stroud
Illustrations © 1998 Caroline Jayne Church
This book has been typeset in Letraset Arta

Printed in China

British Library Cataloguing in Publication Data:
a catalogue record for this book is available
from the British Library.

ISBN-13: 978-1-4063-0295-0
ISBN-10: 1-4063-0295-3
www.walkerbooks.co.uk